Wood harvesting with hand tools

Wood harvesting with hand tools

An illustrated training manual

International Labour Office   Geneva

ISBN 92-2-106217-1

First published 1987

Printed in France   SAD

CONTENTS

- o 0 o -

INTRODUCTION

This training manual updates and amalgamates the following previous ILO publications:

- Felling and cross-cutting of tropical trees in natural
  forests (1969); and

- Selection and maintenance of logging hand tools (1970).

These publications were prepared by B. Strehlke, on the basis of
substantial inputs from H. Gläser and R. Wettstein and with illustrations by B. Schmidle. The first of these two publications
dealt with axes, hand saws and chain saws. Its English version
has been out of print for several years. In 1980, in collaboration with the FAO, the section dealing with chain saws was expanded
to include work in man-made forests and chain-saw maintenance and
this was published separately under the title:

- Chainsaws in tropical forests (Rome, FAO/ILO, 1980).

During the last decade, the use of chain saws has spread in-
creasingly to the developing countries where they are found in
commercial logging operations, especially in countries with
higher wage levels. However, wood harvesting with manual tools
continues on a large scale and, with the shift of emphasis to
trees grown by rural people, it will gain more importance in the
years to come.

It is for this reason that a need was felt to compile information on basic wood harvesting, excluding machines and techniques which in many developing countries are out of reach of the rural popula- tion. This view was fully supported by the participants in an FAO/ECE/ILO Workshop on the Transfer of Basic Technology, held in 1986.

For several years it looked as if experience in efficient basic logging and supplies of hand tools of adequate quality would be- come less and less available. This trend has changed thanks to the manufacture of improved forestry tools in several developing countries and the reappearance of logging hand tools in the cata- logues of some of the major dealers in forestry tools and equipment.

Attempts have also been made in Central Europe and Scandinavia to keep alive experience in manual logging accumulated in previous periods and to encourage further improvement of manual tools and techniques. An example of this is the logging sulky of which a bogie type has been developed only recently.

This manual is addressed primarily to trainers, extension workers, work supervisors and foremen.

As in the three publications mentioned above, an attempt has been made to use simple terms and to describe as much as possible by means of drawings. Users are encouraged to translate the text into other languages and to copy illustrations in any way they might find useful for training purposes.

The reader interested in supplementary information is referred to the following publications:

-   Equipment planning guides for vocational and technical
    training and education programmes: No. 17 - Forestry
    (Geneva, ILO, 1981);

-   Basic technology in forest operations (Rome, FAO, 1982);

-   Swedish forestry techniques with possible applications in
    the Third World (Spånga, SIDA, 1983);

-   Handbook on appropriate technology for forestry operations
    in developing countries (Helsinki, FINNIDA, 1986).

The present publication was compiled by B. Strehlke in collaboration with E. Fosser. Hazel Cecconi edited and typed the text and Michel Bagès amended and supplemented the drawings. DANIDA provided the finance.

HAND TOOLS FOR WOOD HARVESTING

The following tools are needed for efficient manual wood harvesting:

(1)   Axe (weight between 0.8 and 1.5 kg)

(2)   One-man bow saw (length approx. 1 m)

(3)   Cross-cut saw (length usually 1.20-1.60 m)

(4)   Machete

(5)   Splitting hammer (weight about 2.5 kg)

(6)   Wedges (for felling, cross-cutting and splitting)

(7)   Turning hook

(8)   Timber tong and timber pick

(9)   Measuring stick or tape measure

(10)   Caliper (to measure diameter)

(11)   Debarking spade

More detailed information is given in: Equipment planning guide
for vocational and technical training and education programmes:
No. 17 - Forestry (Geneva, ILO, 1981).

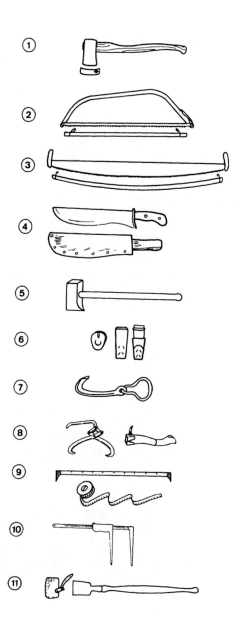

FILES

The following types of file will commonly be used for maintaining
forest tools. An effort has been made to keep these to the minimum to simplify stocking and distribution.

For cross-cut saws

Millsaw file, 20 cm, single cut, smooth (22.4 cuts per cm), flat
with two round edges for sharpening cutter and raker teeth and for
deepening small gullets **(1)**.

A worn file of this sort can be used for jointing the saw and for
lowering the raker.

Round file, 25 cm, constant diameter of 12.5 mm for deepening the
big gullets between rakers **(2)**.

For axes and other edged tools

Millsaw file, 25 cm, single cut, tapered or blunt for reshaping
(3).

For tool handles

Wood rasps are used for shaping wooden handles **(4)**. They must
never be used on metal.

File handles

A file or rasp must never be used without a handle **(5)**. The
handle should have a length of 12 cm.

Care of files

When file or rasp teeth become clogged, they must be cleaned with
a wire brush (file card) which must be kept clean and dry **(6)**.

Files must never be allowed to become rusty, knocked or dropped
and are best kept in a canvas holder when not in use.

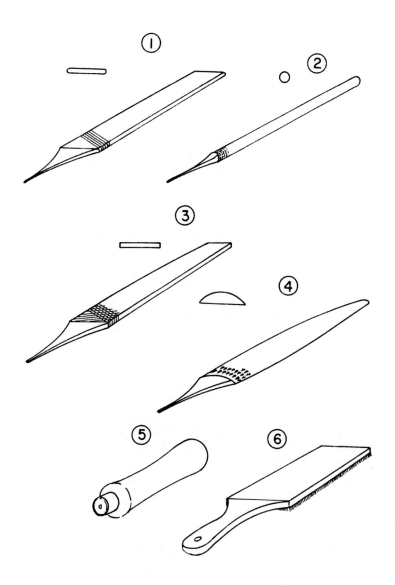

GRINDSTONES AND WHETSTONES

For sharpening axes, debarking spades and other cutting tools,
revolving grindstones operated by hand or foot are used for regular overhauls (1). They should have a minimum diameter of 50 cm
and a minimum width of 10 cm, be made of sandstone or appropriate
artificial material and be used with water. When not in use, the
stone must be kept dry to prevent moisture softening the part of
the stone under water. From time to time, the stone must be
"dressed", that is, restored to its original circular shape.

Grindstones can easily be made locally from 20 litres of good
quality cement and 50 litres of quartzitic sand with 1 mm or
smaller particle size. The sand must be sieved (e.g. with mos-
quito netting), be washed and clean from clay or salt. In
addition, an iron tube or rod is needed, about 60 cm length and
2 cm diameter with a nail welded to its middle.

The grindstone is made in a wooden mould (2) which is set up in
a shady place. The mould is approximately 50 by 50 cm in size
and 15 cm high. It consists of two parts (2a) which are placed
on a board (2b) resting on two supports (2c).

Exactly in the centre of the mould the iron rod is placed, forming
a perfect right angle with the mould and securely held in position
by small boards nailed on the mould (3a).

After filling the mould with mortar and compacting it carefully,
the grindstone is left to dry for about three days. Some sprink-
ling with water may be required to avoid too rapid drying.

After removing the grindstone from the mould, the stone is placed
in a trestle with a piece of an old tyre fitted underneath as a
water container (4a).

This type of grindstone is also handy for sharpening agricultural
tools such as hoes and spades and should be available in any
village.

In addition to grindstones, whetstones are necessary where edged
tools are in use for frequently touching them up during the day.
They are also used for finishing axes after grindstone work and
saws and axes after filing. Whetstones with a coarse and a fine
side, of pocket size (5 by 10 cm), are required (5).

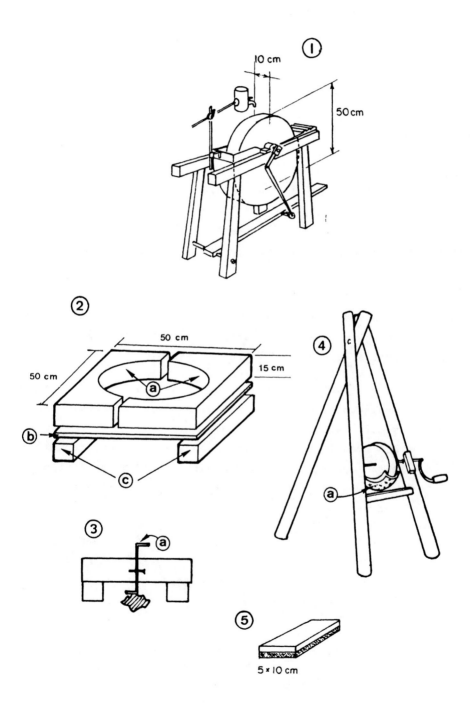

SPLITTING HAMMER AND WEDGES

To avoid the saw blade getting caught in the saw cut (pinching),
and to lift the tree into the intended direction of fall and for
splitting wood, a splitting hammer **(1)** and wedges **(2)** are needed.

The splitting hammer should have a weight of about 2.5 kg and
a straight handle about 90 cm long. For splitting, the edge
should be kept sharp.

Wedges should preferably be made from aluminium alloys. They can
also be made from hard wood. Steel wedges have the disadvantage
of being very heavy and dangerous if splinters break off.

Three types of wedges are suggested for use:

Type **2a** is a wedge commonly used for tree felling with a rather
large surface and a narrow angle, opening up closed saw
cuts even under very high pressure.

Type **2b** consists of a metal shoe and a wooden head which can be
replaced after wear. Additionally, the wooden head is
secured with a metal ring. This type of wedge has a
wider angle and therefore opens the saw cut farther up
than type **2a**. In the absence of a metal shoe, the head
of a wooden wedge may be fitted with an iron ring to
reduce wear.

Type **2c**, made from metal, is very convenient for cross-cutting
and felling. It can be carried in the pocket and should
be inserted in the saw cut as a measure of precaution
before the saw cut closes.

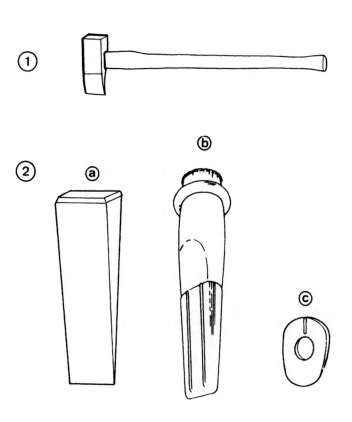

MAKING TOOL HANDLES

This simple construction made from wood and two pieces of an old
tyre **(1a)** is very practical for holding a piece of wood when
making a handle.

The vice is closed when the platform is down **(1b)**. It opens when
the platform is lifted **(2a)**. The tool is firmly held between the
two rubber pieces when the worker is standing on the platform.
His elbow height should then correspond to the height of the opening of the vice.

Good tool handles, for instance of axes, hooks and hoes, are
extremely important to ensure that work can be done conveniently
and efficiently. The handle should fit the worker (size of hand,
length of arm, height) and the size and weight of the tool. It
should be made from suitable wood in order to last for a long time.

The vice can be used for other purposes as well, such as holding
an axe during sharpening.

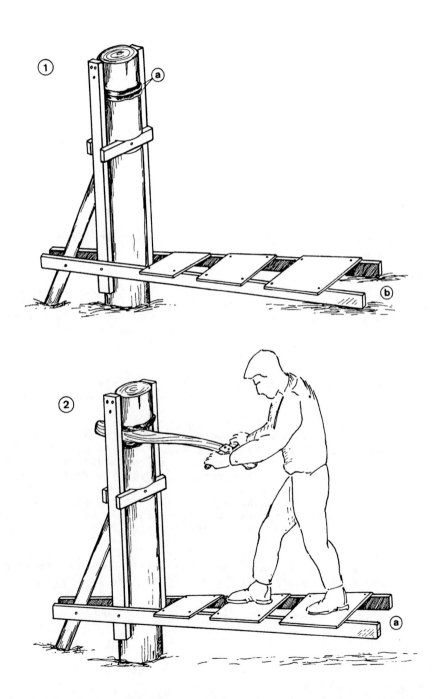

USE AND TYPES OF AXES

In traditional wood harvesting, the axe is used as a universal
tool for felling, debranching, cross-cutting, splitting and
debarking.

The main advantages of axe work are the simple tool outfit and
easy maintenance.

However, it is heavy work and may waste a lot of wood and cause
many accidents, including very serious ones.

Axe work should be restricted to the felling of very small trees,
to preparation for the felling of larger ones and to debranching.

Axes made by local blacksmiths may be quite good for traditional
use if they are properly hardened and well shafted.

The axe consists of a steel head fitted to a wooden handle. The
most important part of the head (1) is the blade (1a), ending in
the edge (1b). The wooden handle is fitted into the eye (1c).
Modern axes are shaped like a wedge and have an oval eye which
prevents the handle from turning in the eye.

Special types of axes can be used for felling and debranching.
However, in most cases a universal axe is used for both jobs.

For professional work, the type of axe shown in the picture is
recommended (2). The weight should be from 0.8 to 1.5 kg, the
length of the handle from 60-80 cm, depending on the length of the
worker's arms (3). The handle should have fawnfoot shape (2) and
be made of strong wood. Workers should be able to make handles and
to replace broken handles themselves. During transport, the axe
blade should be secured with a protective cover which can be made
easily, e.g. from a worn bicycle tyre (2a).

To keep the axe sharp, repeated maintenance is needed during the
course of the day using a whetstone (see page 8).

①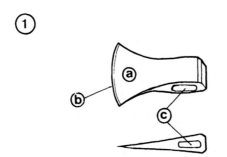

②

③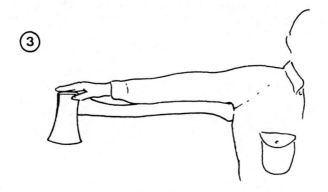

MAINTAINING AN AXE

Taper

The axe blade has a curved taper towards the edge. During sharpening it is important that the correct taper is maintained.

Heavy axes and axes used to cut hard wood and frozen wood require
a stronger blade close to the cutting edge **(1a)**.

Lighter axes and axes used for soft wood should be thinner close
to the cutting edge **(1b)**.

Although wood of coniferous trees is usually soft, branches may
be very hard and axes may require the same taper as for hard wood.

Taper gauge

The taper of new axes is usually suitable for average conditions.
A gauge can be made from a piece of metal sheet corresponding to
the taper of the new axe **(2a)**. This gauge can be used during
maintenance. If the axe "bites", the taper is too small and if
the axe does not penetrate enough into the wood, the taper is too
big. Adjustments are made during maintenance and when the taper
corresponds to the requirements, the taper gauge can be adjusted
accordingly.

Daily maintenance

Hone the axe several times daily with a whetstone **(3)**. Use water
or spit on the whetstone to keep it moist. Honing is done down-
wards on one side with the handle down **(3a)** and on the other side
with the handle up **(3b)**.

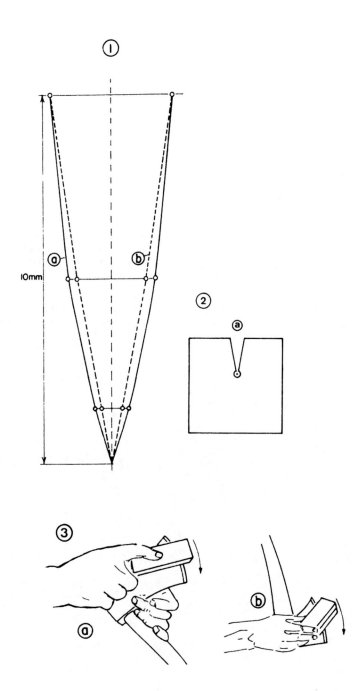

① ⓐ ⓑ 10mm

② ⓐ

③ ⓐ ⓑ

MAINTAINING AN AXE (continued)

Major overhaul

This is done at intervals of about a week or longer depending on the use of the axe. Major overhaul is done by the following steps:

- Check curve of edge with a new axe or a curve gauge (1). A curve gauge can be made locally from a metal sheet (1a), using a new axe to copy the correct curve.

- If necessary, correct curve with millsaw file (page 6), holding the axe in a vice (2).

- Grind axe blade on grindstone in zone 3a, by moving the axe from right to left (4) and at the same time up and down (5). Grind zone 3b only at longer intervals, if necessary, by moving the axe from left to right (4).

- Final honing is done as for daily maintenance with a whetstone to remove burrs and to polish the surface of the axe (see 3, previous page).

If a grindstone is not available, a millsaw file can be used for sharpening. Care must be taken to file a correct taper. Always move file away from the cutting edge.

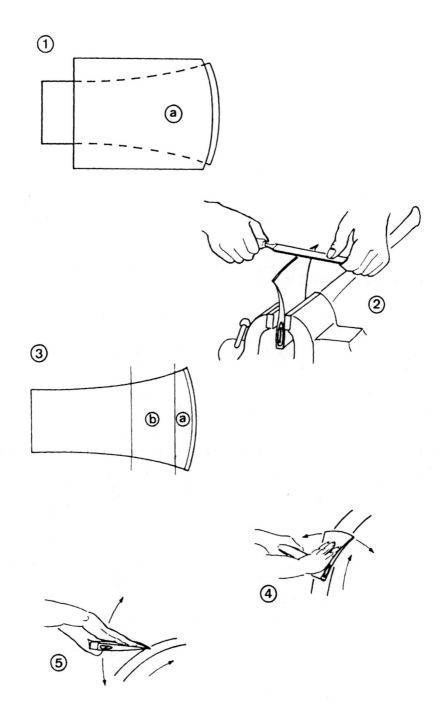

MAKING AN AXE HANDLE

To make an axe handle, hardwood of high elasticity and strength
is taken from the butt end of a young tree or from the outer
zones of an old one. The wood must be well seasoned. It should
have straight fibres and be free of knots and bends.

A scantling is sawn or squared with an axe out of a suitable
piece of wood (1). Annual rings should run through the scantling
as indicated in the drawing (2a). The scantling must be well
seasoned before the handle is made.

A model of a fawnfoot handle is used for drawing the outline of
the handle on the scantling (2b). The model can be copied from
a new handle on a piece of cardboard.

A bow saw is used for making cuts into the wood to be taken off
from the scantling (2c).

An axe can be used for shaping the outline of the handle.

Final shaping is done with a spokeshave (3), if available, and
a wood rasp (see page 6).

The handle is finished by polishing with sandpaper (4), a piece
of glass (for instance, window glass), or a knife.

Making an axe handle is easier if a vice can be used (see page 12).

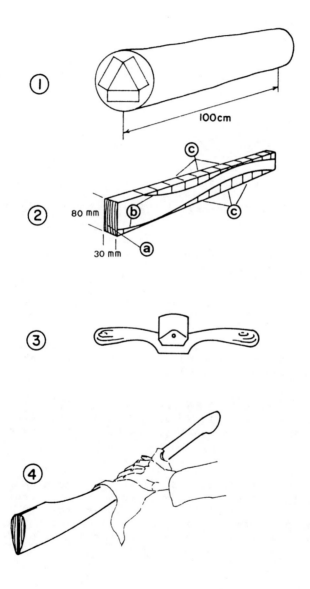

① 100cm

② 80 mm
30 mm
ⓐ ⓑ ⓒ ⓒ

③

④

SHAFTING AN AXE

When shafting an axe, care must be taken to ensure:

- that the blade and the handle are in exactly the same plane (1);

- that the centre of the blade touches the surface if the axe is placed with the blade and the end of the handle on a level surface (2).

Shafting is done by the following steps:

- Fit the handle exactly to the eye of the axe, preferably with a wood rasp (3).

- Put handle into the eye (4) and test for correct alignment (1, 2).

- Take the handle out and cut with a knife or axe to the depth of the eye (5).

- Put the handle into the eye again and drive a small hardwood wedge into the saw cut (6).

- Test for correct alignment (1, 2). If necessary, adjust alignment with the wood rasp after having taken off the head of the axe once more.

- If the alignment is correct, put 2 small nails across the handle, and wedge it above the head of the axe (6a), saw off the protruding part of the handle and wedge about 1 cm above nails.

Note: If an axe is reshafted, drive the remaining wood out of the eye either from the unwedged side or from the wedged side once nails and wedge have been removed. Never burn wood still remaining in the eye: by doing this, the axe's temper would be lost and it would become useless.

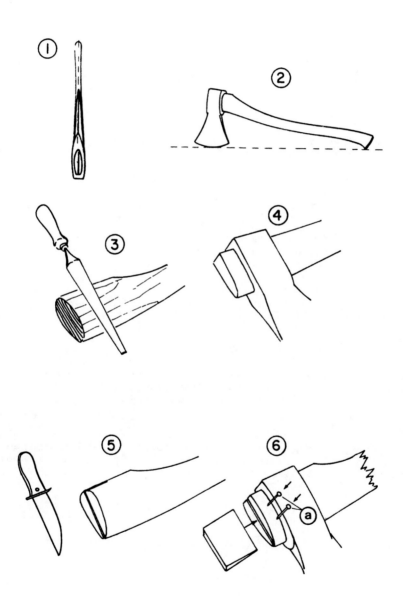

USE AND TYPES OF BOW SAWS

Bow saws are handy for felling and cross-cutting small trees provided the wood is not too hard.

For professional use, the bow saw should consist of a high-quality
oval steel frame holding a thin blade under high tension **(1)**. A
protective cover is needed to guard the blade during transport **(1a)**.

A one-man bow saw with an asymmetric frame of approx. 100 cm
length is recommended **(1)**. There are also models with a sym-
metric frame and one side of the bow extended into a handle
which allows more force in cutting but restricts movement if
space is narrow **(1b)**.

For a frame of 100 cm length, the corresponding saw blades **(2)**
are 91.5 cm long and usually have hard-pointed peg teeth **(2a)**
or raker teeth **(2b)**.

When a hard-pointed blade loses its set and starts pinching, it
should be re-set with setting pliers **(3)**.

When the blade becomes dull, it can be re-sharpened with a whetstone **(4)**. If the saw runs to one side, the whetstone should be
used on the side to which it is running **(5)**.

Hard-pointed blades wear out after some time and must then be
discarded. Great care must be taken during cutting to avoid
contact with soil, sand and stones.

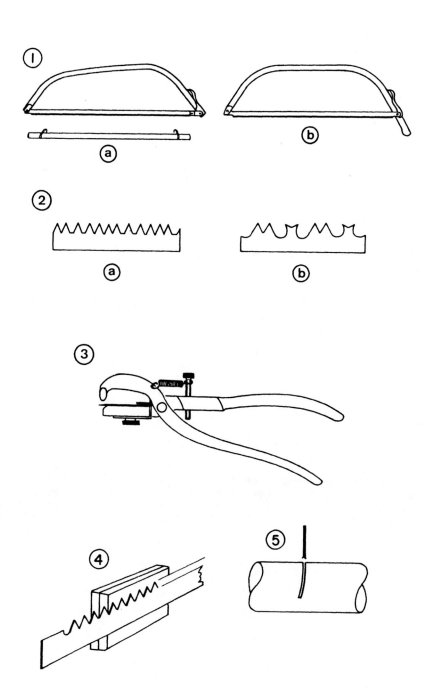

TYPES OF CROSS-CUT SAWS

If cross-cut saws are used, a comprehensive tool outfit is required. The saw must be well maintained in order to make the job
easy and efficient. Properly maintained saws require less energy
in use and increase production.

The saw should be made of high-quality steel. For large trees,
a straight-back type of saw is preferable **(1a)** and for small to
medium trees a hollow-back type. The cutting edge should be
thicker than the back in order to reduce friction and the risk
of "binding". The length of the saw should be 100 cm plus the
diameter of the tree. The saw should be fitted with detachable
handles **(1b)** which can easily be screwed on and off. A protective
cover **(1c)** is needed to guard the cutting edge during transport.

Peg-tooth type saws are common because they are easy to maintain
(2a).

Raker-tooth type saws are preferred by professional workers.
They cut faster but require more skill in maintenance **(2b)**.

Saw teeth must do three things:

-   cut through the fibres;

-   break loose the cut fibres;

-   remove the loose fibres (sawdust) from the kerf.

In peg-tooth saws, these three things are done by one tooth. In
raker-tooth saws the first of the three actions is done by a group
of cutters cutting on alternate sides of the kerf. The second and
third actions are done by the raker following the group of cutters.

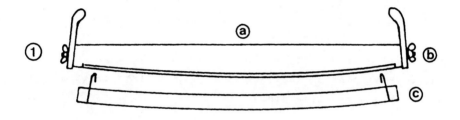

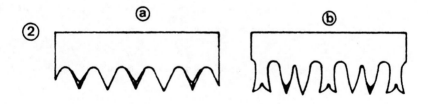

MAINTENANCE TOOLS FOR CROSS-CUT SAWS

The following maintenance tools are necessary for <u>peg-tooth</u> type
saws:

(1a)	Millsaw file (single cut)	**(1e)**	Setting iron
(1b)	Jointer, commercial or self-made using a worn file	**(1f)**	Setting indicator, commercial or self-made
(1c)	Angle gauge	**(1g)**	Whetstone
(1d)	Filing grid	**(1h)**	Filing vice

(The self-made setting indicator consists of a piece of wood with
three metal pins of the same length in a fixed position and an
adjustable screw-type pin.)

For <u>raker-tooth</u> type saws, the same maintenance tools are needed,
except for the following differences:

- a raker adjuster (or a combined raker adjuster and shaper)
  (2a) is necessary; and

- a setting hammer **(2b)** and a setting anvil **(2c)** replace the
  setting iron.

29

①
ⓐ ⓑ ⓒ ⓓ ⓔ ⓕ ⓖ ⓗ

②
ⓐ ⓑ ⓒ

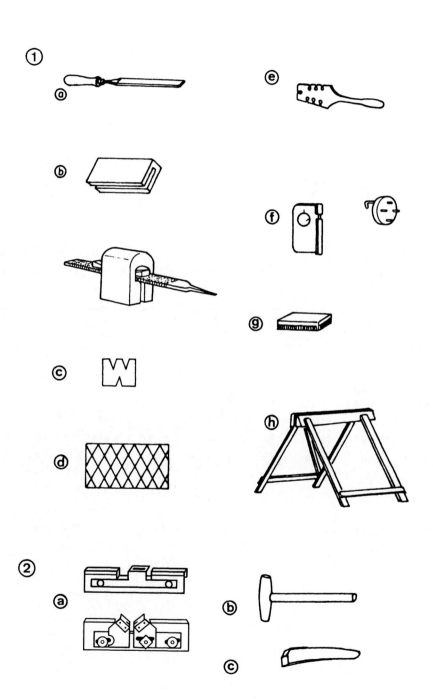

FILING VICES, SELF-MADE

A filing vice holds the saw firmly in position during maintenance.
Peg-tooth saws are held vertically. Filing vices for raker-tooth
saws must hold the saw-blade firmly in vertical and oblique positions that can be easily changed. Opening and closing should be
easy. Saw vices must have a length of at least 50 cm, preferably
more. They must be steady. The saw should be held at the height
of the worker's elbow allowing a comfortable working position
whether he is standing or sitting.

A filing vice can easily be made from a standing tree of no or
little commercial value sawn off at elbow height. As required,
vertical and oblique cuts are made into the stump. The saw can
be firmly held in these cuts by using small wooden wedges **(1)**.

The Swedish saw vice **(2)** is built of two boards **(2a)** enclosing a
wedge-shaped centre piece **(2b)** and connected by three leather
straps **(2c)**. Four wooden legs **(2d)** are screwed on to these boards
When the vice is erected, the saw is held between one of the two
boards and the centre piece in a vertical or oblique position.

The Swedish saw vice can be made easily from locally-available
materials and is easily transportable.

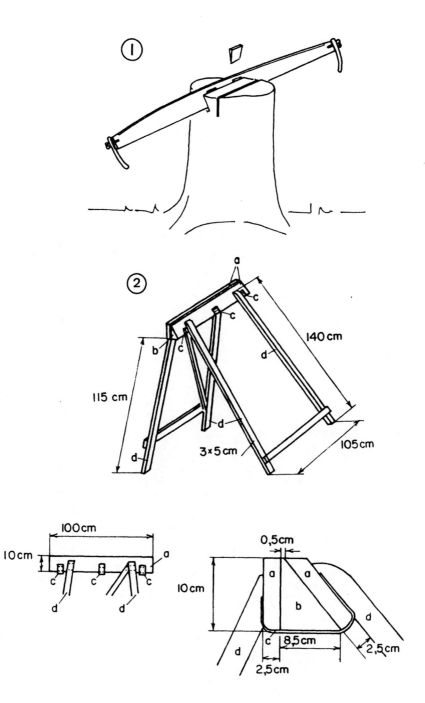

FILING VICES, COMMERCIALLY-MADE

Commercially-made filing vices are available in various types.
Two handy examples are given:

The Swiss filing bench has the advantage of enabling the worker
to sit during filing (1).

An engineer's vice can be used as a filing vice by inserting two
pieces of wood in a vertical position connected with flap hinges
between the vice jaws. An oblique position of the saw can be
arranged using two wedges (2).

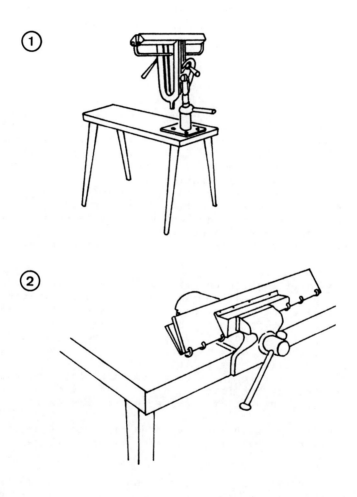

MAINTAINING A PEG-TOOTH CROSS-CUT SAW

The following measures are recommended for triangular teeth:

Hardness of wood	Distance between points of two teeth	Height of tooth	Width of gullet between two teeth
Hard	17 mm	16 mm	6.0 mm
Soft	9 mm	12 mm	0.5 mm
Mixed hard and soft	14 mm	15 mm	3.7 mm

Maintenance starts with jointing while the saw is firmly held in a vertical position by the filing vice. The jointer is run along the saw teeth using very little pressure (1). In normal use, the teeth in the middle of the saw will wear more quickly than those at the end. This is adjusted by increased pressure at the beginning and the end of the jointing stroke.

The jointing is continued until all cutter teeth show a small "flat" and jointing should stop when this happens. One or a few (if evenly distributed) badly worn or broken teeth are not considered. Further jointings will bring them back into the tooth line.

Cutter teeth filing is done with a 20 cm millsaw file using horizontal strokes parallel to the lines of a grid attached to the vice (2). The sharpening angle marked on the grid (2a) is 70° for hard wood and 60° for soft wood. These angles may be copied from figure 3. The top angle (2b) is 38° for hard and soft wood. A gauge is needed to check the sharpening angle and the top angle (4). During filing, the gullet should be lowered at the same time (5). First file one side of the saw, tooth by tooth, and then turn the saw and file the other side. Care must be taken to stop filing when the flat is about to disappear.

Deburring is done with the whetstone, the fine side of which is run lightly along both sides (as for raker-tooth saws, see page 38).

Setting is carried out with a setting indicator (6a) and a special saw set (6b). The correct set is 0.3-0.4 mm for hard wood and 0.5-0.6 mm for soft wood.

Note: Badly worn saws may need gulleting before sharpening begins. This is best done after having marked the gullet depth and position (7a). The round edge of the millsaw file is used for gulleting (7b).

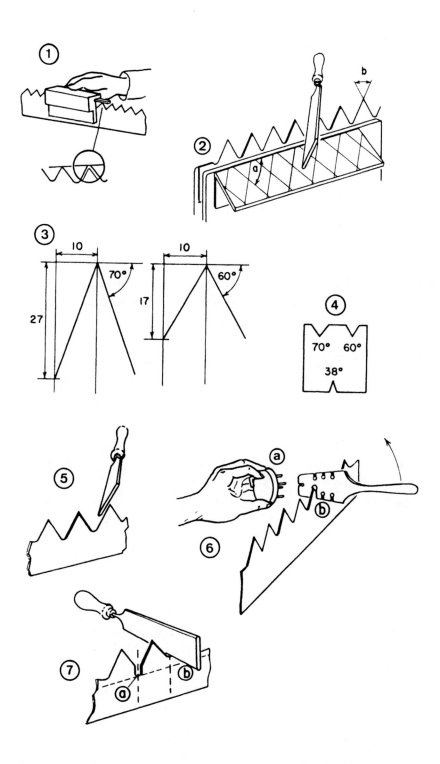

TYPES OF RAKER-TOOTH CROSS-CUT SAWS

The raker-tooth cross-cut saw is the most efficient type of saw
for felling and cross-cutting. This type of saw is recommended
for professional use.

There are two types: one raker followed by two cutters (Champion
teeth BM[1]) for harder wood **(1)** and one raker followed by four
cutters (Lance teeth, 4 YM[1]) for softer wood **(2)**.

The raker's work can be compared with that of a plane. It re-
moves the fibres **(3b)** which are cut on both sides of the kerf by
the cutters **(3a)**. The raker must be slightly shorter than the
cutters so that it will not break off uncut fibres. However, if
too short, it will not sufficiently break loose the cut fibres
and the cutters will jam in the kerf. A gullet of sufficient
depth is needed to hold and transport the sawdust **(3c)**.

Correct raker depth produces long chips with clean edges **(4)**;
if the raker depth is too long, chips tend to have whiskers **(5)**;
if too short, fine sawdust is produced.

---

[1] According to International Organisation for Standardisa-
tion.

MAINTAINING A RAKER-TOOTH CROSS-CUT SAW

Maintenance work follows the same pattern as for peg-tooth saws
except that, additionally, raker adjustment is needed. The saw
is held at all times in a vertical position during maintenance
work.

Jointing is done in exactly the same way as for peg-tooth saws (1).

Raker adjustment. The raker adjuster, correctly set, is placed
over a raker (2). Holding the tool firmly against the saw, the
raker is filed flush with the tool guide plate (2a). The raker
depth should be 0.2-0.5 mm for hard wood and 0.6-1.0 mm for soft
wood (2b). The correct depth must be found under working conditions and will be indicated by properly-shaped saw chips.

Raker filing is done after adjusting the raker height (3). It
is continued until the flat is as small as possible. Horizontal
file strokes are used (3a). The raker angle should be 90°. It
can be checked easily during filing with the top end of the millsaw file (3b).

Cutter teeth filing is done with the saw in the oblique position
(4). A top angle of 70° and a side angle of 35° must be produced.
Filing strokes should not exceed 60 per minute. The full length
of the file is used and an even pressure put on the file. Check
the angles with the gauge frequently and when the flat almost
disappears, tap the top of the tooth with the file handle or small
piece of wood. This gives a true picture of how much flat is left.
The last strokes with the file must be very gentle. Sharpening is
finished when the flat is just about to disappear.

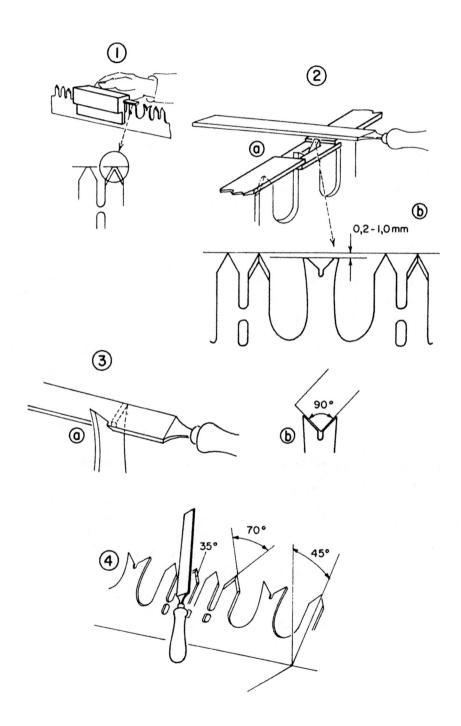

MAINTAINING A RAKER-TOOTH CROSS-CUT SAW (continued)

Deburring. Put the saw in a vertical position. The fine side of
the whetstone is run along both sides of the saw to remove burrs
(1). Be careful not to touch the sharp teeth with the fingers.

Setting (2). Check that the saw is held very firmly in the vice.
For a right-handed man, the left arm is put over the saw, taking
care not to catch the saw with the arm or body, and the anvil held
in the left hand. Those teeth with the bevels towards the body
are set first. The anvil is placed against the back of the cutter.
The cutter is set with short and firm strokes of the setting hammer
held in the right hand (2a, 2b).

The setting indicator is used to check the set of each tooth (3).
The correct saw set for hard wood is 0.1-0.2 mm, for soft wood
0.2-0.4 mm (4). Insufficient set is corrected at once by further
hammer strokes. If the set is too great it is removed with the
setting hammer after the position of the anvil has been changed
(5). After setting one side, the saw is turned round and the
other side is set.

Note: The first six teeth on either end of the saw need no setting

Setting normally follows cutter teeth filing but the order can also
be reversed.

Deepening of gullets. At intervals of about four weeks, it is
necessary to deepen the gullets on the cutters (6a) and the gullets
between the rakers (6b) with the millsaw file and the big gullets
between the rakers and the cutters (6c) with the round file.

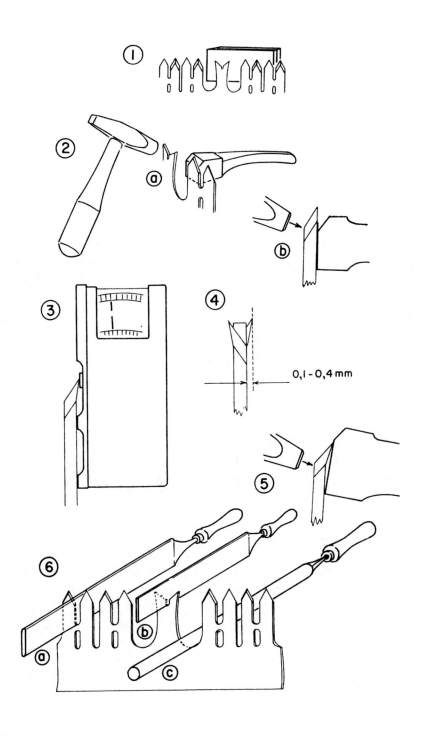

0,1 - 0,4 mm

MAJOR OVERHAUL OF CROSS-CUT SAWS

If saws become badly out of tooth line, it is necessary to adjust
the tooth line. This can best be done by using a new saw which
is properly shaped as a model. Its tooth line is marked with a
scribe on the old saw **(1)**. A second line is drawn underneath at
the correct gullet depth. This can also be done after jointing
with a scribe attached to the jointer **(2)**. The position of tooth
points is also marked on the old saw to avoid incorrect spacing.

If a new saw is not available, a thin flexible board (or a
straight-back saw) can be used to draw the desired curve **(3)**.
It is fixed on both ends and bent in the middle to the correct
tooth line shape. If a straight line **(3)** is drawn between the
two ends of the board, the correct curve is obtained if the
middle of the board is bent outward **(3b)** by 7 cm for 1.5 m saw
length, by 8 cm for 2.0 m saw length and 9 cm for 2.5 m saw
length.

Reshaping the curve according to the new tooth line marked on
the saw is facilitated if shears can be used instead of files.
Shears may be found in central workshops.

Use of a press

In central workshops, it may also be useful to provide a press
for deepening gullets and reshaping worn saws **(4)**. This saves
files and time.

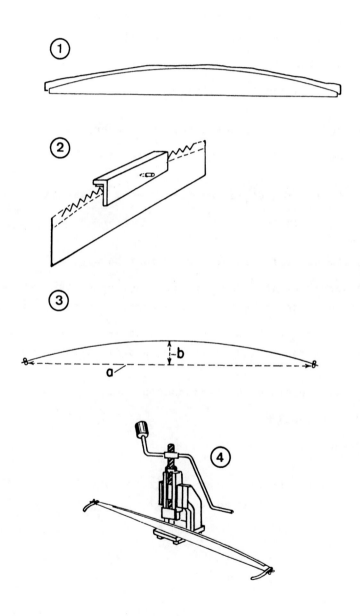

CLOTHING, PERSONAL PROTECTIVE EQUIPMENT, FIRST-AID EQUIPMENT

Workers should wear:

(1) Long-sleeved shirt or jacket, preferably in a warning colour, fitting neither too loosely nor too tightly.

(2) Long trousers.

(3) Boots with non-slip soles.

In felling operations, the worker <u>must</u> wear:

(4) Safety helmet with ventilation holes.

During the felling of large-sized trees, it may be advisable to use:

(5) Knee protectors.

The following first-aid equipment must be available:

(6) A pocket first-aid kit containing roller bandages and standard dressing for open wounds, carried by the worker.

(7) A full first-aid kit for treating serious accidents, to be kept at the work site for a group of workers.

During rainy periods, workers should have:

(8) Rubber boots.

(9) Raincoats.

Simple shelters should be available for use during breaks as a protection against rain or sun **(10)**.

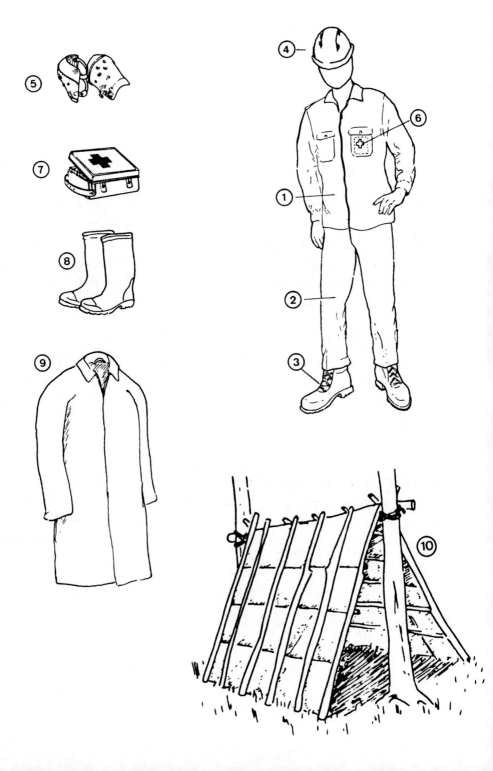

FOOD, NUTRITION AND REST

Wood harvesting is heavy work and over a period of time is tiring. The worker must therefore be in a good state of health and be well fed.

He should have a meal before starting work and eat during breaks.

Under severe climatic conditions (very hot weather or humid, tropical climate), not more than six hours of productive work can be expected. During a six-hour working day, two meal breaks of at least 30 minutes each should be taken (after the first two hours of work and again two hours later).

Food should be sufficiently rich in starches (rice, maize, wheat, millet, bananas, cassava); in proteins (beans, eggs, meat, fish); in fats (olive oil, coconut oil, cheese, butter); and in vitamins (fruit, vegetables).

During hard work and in hot weather, the body can lose 3 to 6 litres of liquid per day. This must be replaced. Workers should carry a container with boiled water, tea or other beverages and drink not only when thirsty but also at regular intervals during the day. Care must be taken to replace the salt lost through sweating.

47

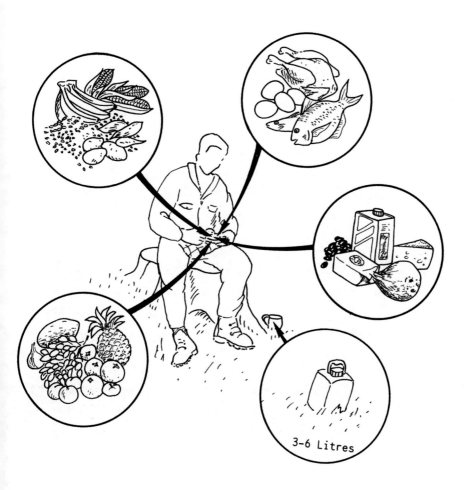

3-6 Litres

WORKING POSTURES AND MOVEMENTS

Heavy physical work can be made easier by proper working postures
and working movements.

Sawing can become very tiring and quite inefficient if the saw
is pulled by the arms towards the body, if the body remains stiff
and upright and consequently only short strokes can be made.

To make the job less tiring and more efficient, the saw should
work along its full length and the load should be carried not
only by the arm muscles but by the whole body swinging backwards
and forwards and supporting the movement of the saw.

Efficient working techniques in the use of bow saws (1) and cross-
cut saws (2) are indicated in the illustration, showing the change
in working position. The same principles apply to other jobs,
such as debarking (3).

Manual wood harvesting often involves heavy lifting and carrying
of loads. In such work, the back should be kept straight to
avoid excessive strain and the strong muscles of the legs should
be used for lifting (4).

49

WORKING POSTURES AND MOVEMENTS (continued)

In axe work, the whole body moves and supports the stroke by
changing the weight from the leg away from the cut to the leg
near the cut while the upper hand slides down the handle. If
the worker masters the left-hand grip **(1)**, **(2)** and the right-
hand grip **(3)**, work is safer and less strenuous.

WORK PLANNING AND ORGANISATION

Wood harvesting must be well planned and organised in order to
make the best use of the raw material while keeping labour input
and production cost low and minimising damage to the environment.

A variety of different harvesting systems can be applied depending on the wood species, size and assortment (fuelwood, poles or
logs), type of forest (man-made or natural), type of cut (thinning
or clear cut), kind of regeneration (artificial, coppice, natural),
terrain (flat, steep, swampy), accessibility (roads, waterways)
and means of transport (manual, animal, motorised).

In all these cases, good planning and organisation of work depends
on:

- the assessment of the volume to be harvested;

- the determination of the assortments to be produced;

- the determination of wood storing places, skidding lines
  and felling direction;

- clearly-instructed and skilled supervisors and workers;

- availability of the necessary hand tools and maintenance
  and other equipment;

- clear separation of working areas for individual work teams
  and different operations (felling and transport).

The illustration shows an example of a harvesting map indicating
the forest road network (1), the transport direction (2), the
skidding lines (3), the felling direction (4) and the storage
places for logs (5) and short wood (6).

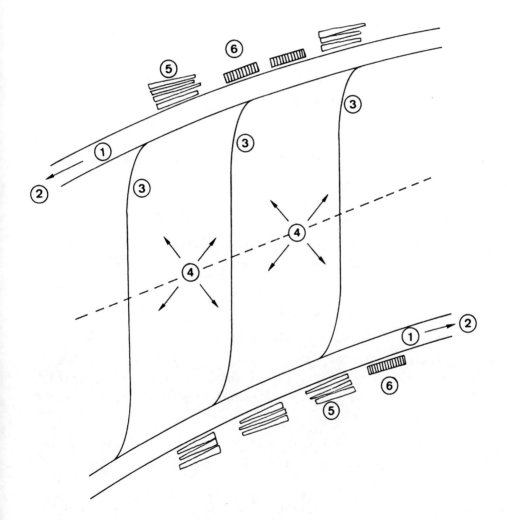

ACCIDENT PREVENTION

Wood harvesting is extremely dangerous. Many workers are killed or severely injured in tree felling and transport. Cutting tools may lead to serious open wounds. Many accidents occur when workers slip, stumble and fall in difficult terrain or on slippery surfaces.

Adequate accident prevention is therefore a basic requirement of any type of wood harvesting.

Workers need to be healthy and in good physical condition. They must be well trained for their jobs. They must strictly observe a definite set of safety rules.

The most important safety rules are the following:

- In tree felling, workers must use safety helmets, wear good shoes with non-slip soles and carry first aid equipment.

- Axes, saws and helping tools should be available in sufficient number and be adequate as regards type and maintenance.

- The felling team must keep a minimum distance of two tree lengths from other workers (1). This distance may be increased to four tree lengths when visibility in the forest is poor. A warning should be given before a tree is about to fall.

- Greatest care is required in controlling trees during felling by an adequate undercut and back cut, leaving a sufficiently strong hinge.

- When the tree falls, the worker must retreat to a safe position and watch out for falling branches (2).

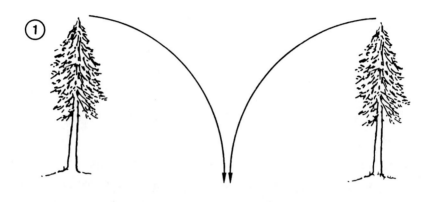

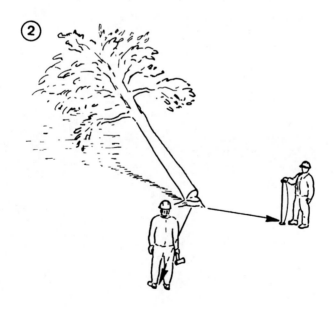

ACCIDENT PREVENTION (continued)

- Particular care is needed to bring lodged trees down safely **(1)**.

- No tree felling should be done in stormy weather.

- During debranching, debarking and cross-cutting, workers must watch out that they are not caught by falling, sliding or turning trees or parts of trees, especially on slopes.

- When axes, debarking spades or splitting hammers are being used, other people must keep clear of the working range.

- Accidents are more frequent towards the end of the day when workers are tired. During this period, harvesting should preferably concentrate on the less dangerous jobs.

The working techniques described in this manual are specifically designed with a view to reducing hazards.

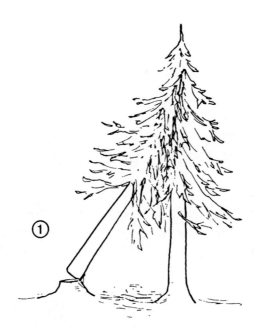

PREPARATION FOR TREE FELLING

The felling direction must be carefully determined (1). This
will depend on the skidding direction, the lean of the tree, the
shape of the crown, the wind, and on obstacles in the way of the
tree's fall, obstacles on the ground and also on the possibility
of retreating safely.

When the felling direction (1a) is determined, the tools are
placed opposite to the felling direction, behind the tree (1b).
The working area around the tree is cleared (1c). Two escape
routes are cleared, as far as is necessary to allow easy retreat,
placed sideways at about 45° angles to the rear (1d).

The base of the tree must be well cleared, using the axe or a
matchet in order to prevent the saw from blunting too quickly (2).

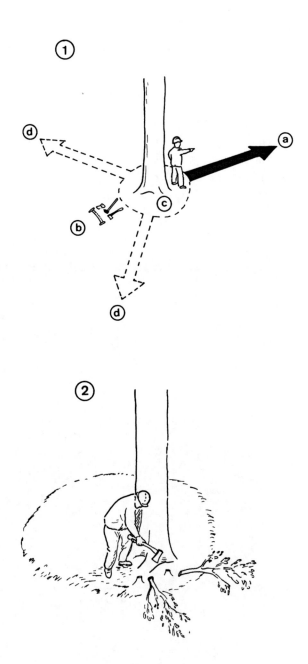

TREE FELLING WITH AXE AND BOW SAW

Small trees are felled with an axe, cutting from both sides **(1)**.

For slightly larger trees, axes are used for making the undercut. In this case, the horizontal cut can be done with the bow saw **(2)**. The back cut should not be made with the axe because too much wood is wasted and it is more difficult to maintain the desired direction of fall **(3)**.

Axe felling of larger trees is allowed only in exceptional cases.

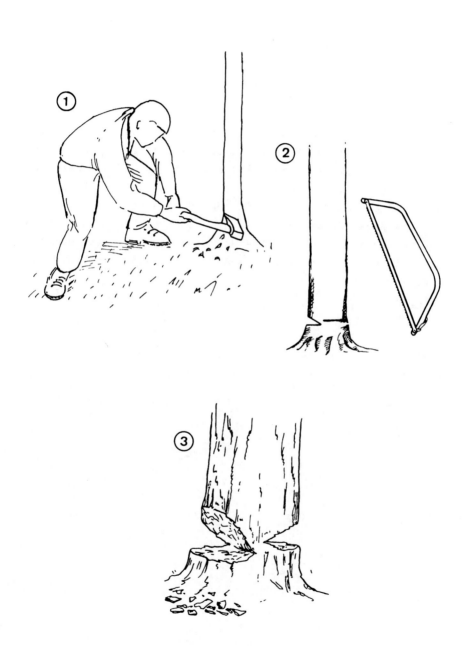

TREE FELLING WITH AXE AND CROSS-CUT SAW

Felling of medium- and large-sized trees is done with the axe
and the cross-cut saw. This process requires special skills and
experience.

A proper undercut **(1a)** and back cut **(1b)** are necessary, leaving
a hinge **(2a)** to guide the tree into the desired direction of fall.
Small lateral cuts **(1c)** and **(2b)** avoid tearing of fibres from the
tree during felling. The depth of the undercut should be about
1/5 to 1/4 of the diameter; it should open at an angle of about
60°. The back cut should be about 2-5 cm higher than the undercut. In very large trees, the undercut may penetrate up to 1/3
of the diameter, depending on shape, and the back cut may be
10-20 cm higher.

Wedging will be necessary to avoid pinching of the saw **(3)**. If
necessary, wedging will also force the tree to fall.

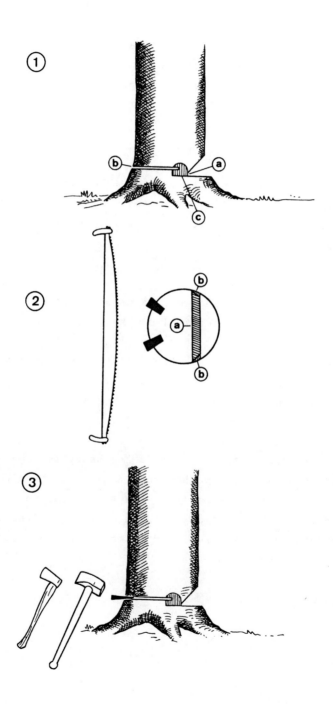

PRECAUTIONS WHEN MAKING THE UNDERCUT AND THE BACK CUT

Accurate felling makes the job safer, facilitates subsequent operations and reduces timber wastage. Felling should therefore be
done with the greatest care and precision. By looking at the
stump, it can easily be seen whether a poor or a good felling job
has been done.

When making the undercut, care must be taken that it points pre-
cisely into the felling direction. This can be checked by standing
in front of the undercut (1). If necessary, the undercut should be
corrected.

Sufficient holding wood which acts as a hinge must always remain
in order to maintain control of the tree so that it does not fall
in any direction other than that intended (2). 2a shows the
correct depth of the back cut. If the cut penetrates as deeply
as indicated by 2b in the picture, the tree is practically loose
and a gust of wind may push it anywhere.

If trees have buttresses, it is necessary to remove them before
making the undercut and back cut, which can then be made with
more precision and ease (3). The buttresses should also be removed to facilitate transport and handling of the log. To make
sure that the cuts are placed in the right position, it helps if
they are marked with an axe.

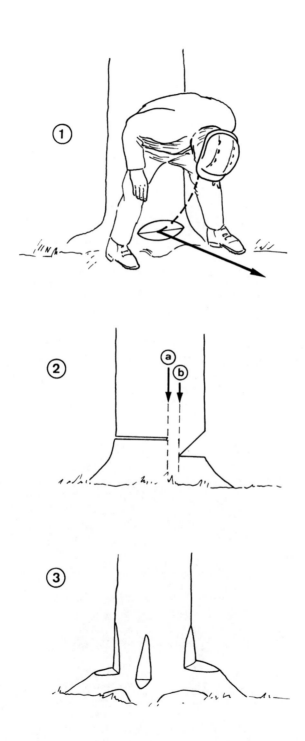

FELLING TREES LEANING INTO THE PLANNED FELLING DIRECTION

Trees leaning into the planned felling direction **(1)** have to be felled particularly carefully in order to avoid danger to the workers, damage to the saw and wastage of timber.

In such a case, the undercut **(2)** must penetrate more deeply into the tree. This may entail preparing the undercut in two steps **(3) and (4)**. When the saw starts pinching, work should continue with the axe.

The back cut **(5)** must be done from both sides and only the remaining wood **(6)** be sawn parallel with the hinge.

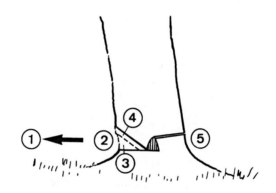

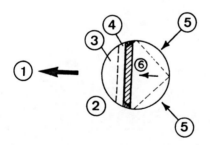

FELLING TREES LEANING TO THE SIDE

A tree can also be felled at an angle of about 30° from the lean.
In this case, the undercut **(a)** should face the intended felling
direction **(b)**. The hinge **(c)** should be kept smaller on the side
of the lean **(d)** and larger on the side to which the tree is to be
felled. In addition, a wedge **(e)** placed on the side of the lean
will help to direct the fall of the tree.

Felling larger trees against the lean is only justified in exceptional cases (e.g. to save young tree growth or near buildings)
and requires special skills, techniques and equipment (e.g. win-
ches).

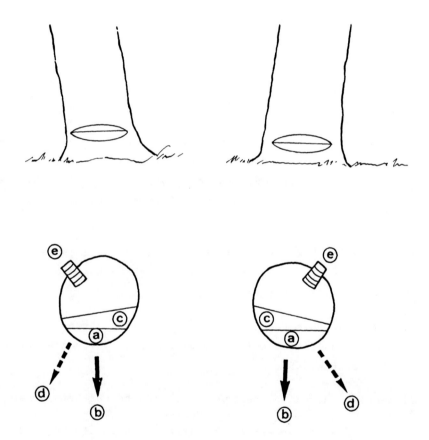

TREE FELLING IN DENSE TROPICAL FORESTS

Felling in dense tropical forests can be particularly dangerous. Dense undergrowth makes it difficult to retreat from the tree during its fall. Dead branches may be hidden in the crown, which is often not visible. For the same reason, it may be difficult to assess the lean of the tree.

Trees may be over-mature and may therefore have hollow or rotten centres.

Trees are often connected to each other with climbers. When the trees fall, they frequently pull down other trees **(1)**. Branches from the falling tree or from neighbouring trees **(2, 3)** are broken off and may swing backwards **(4)**. Climbers are torn off or may break and snap back **(5)**.

The accident risk when felling trees in dense tropical forests is considerably reduced if the area around the base of the tree and the escape routes are well cleared.

Two paths are cleared to a length of 20-30 m beyond the reach of the crown opposite the felling direction. The angle between them should be about 45°.

Climbers attached to the tree must also be cut before sawing begins

It will often be necessary to clean the base of the tree to remove bark and dirt deposited by termites.

Tree harvesting in natural tropical forests still continues to some extent with hand saws although in the large commercial operations chain saws have taken over.

FELLING OF TREES WITH PLANK BUTTRESSES

Plank buttresses are common in tropical trees. They occur in
many tree species once they have grown large.

Large trees with plank buttresses often attain a cylindrical shape
only at a height of 3-5 m above ground level **(1)**. At ground level
the cross-section becomes larger and more irregular **(2)**, **(3)**.

Trees with large plank buttresses may be felled at a convenient
working height while the workers are standing at ground level.

If felling from the ground is not possible, it may be necessary
to build a platform **(4)**, especially in steep terrain. Experienced
workers will be able to do this quite quickly with material available locally. The platform should permit a sufficiently comfortable and safe working position.

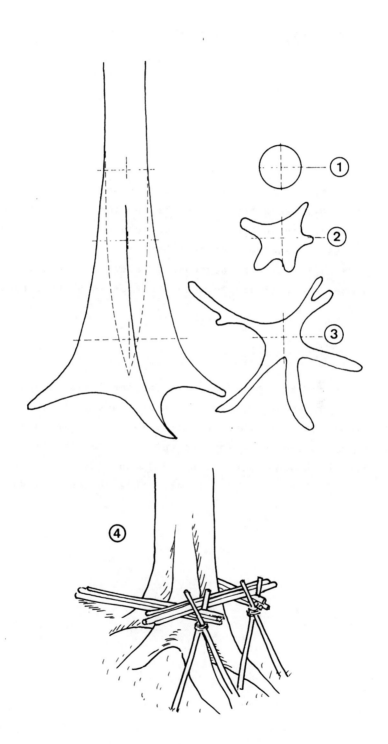

FELLING OF TREES WITH PLANK BUTTRESSES (continued)

If felling is done through the buttresses, the tree is usually
felled into the direction of lean.

The undercut is made to a depth of about one-third of the diameter
(1a). First the horizontal cut is made and then the oblique cut.
The back cut is made about 20 cm higher (or more) than the horizontal cut of the undercut. The cut begins on the side buttresses
(1b) and is finished on the rear buttress **(1c)**. Wedging may be
necessary on the lateral buttress in order to stabilise the tree
and on the rear buttress to push the tree into the direction of
fall **(1d)**.

This technique must be adapted to the particular shape of the
tree. The undercut may, for instance, have to be made in two
buttresses **(2a)**. If there are also two buttresses opposite the
felling direction which have to cut one after the other, the
smaller one should be cut first **(2b)** and then the larger one **(2c)**.
To assist felling, it is again advisable to insert wedges **(2d)**.

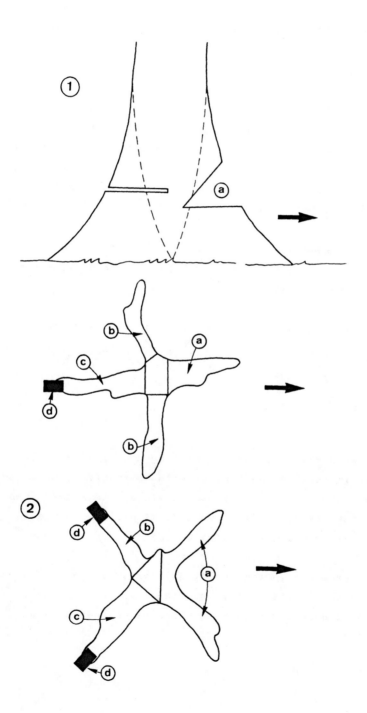

WOOD WASTAGE DUE TO POOR WORKING TECHNIQUES IN FELLING

High stumps are an indication of poor workmanship and insufficient
supervision. Often they are the result of putting felling marks,
which are to be left on the stump for control purposes, too high.
Sometimes workers find it more comfortable to cut about 1 m above
ground level **(1a)**. Except in special cases (e.g. hollow or heavily
buttressed trees), the stump should be as low as possible **(1b)**.
This helps to avoid wastage of wood and because lower stumps make
skidding easier.

Where the wage level is low and the timber price high, the value
of wood left in one stump **(1c)** may correspond to a week's wages or
more of the operator.

The following table gives information on volume loss:

Stump recover-able height	Diameter cm		
	40	60	80
20	0.025	0.057	0.100
40	0.050	0.113	0.200
60	0.075	0.171	0.300

Considerable wood losses in felling can also occur if the tree is
felled without an undercut or with an insufficient undercut **(2)**.
If the undercut is at the same level as, or higher than, the back
cut, there is a risk that wood fibre will be pulled out of the
butt end, reducing the value of the log.

If the undercut is too small **(3a)**, this can be most dangerous
because the tree's fall is no longer properly guided. The tree
may split and this results in considerable wastage on the valuable
butt end.

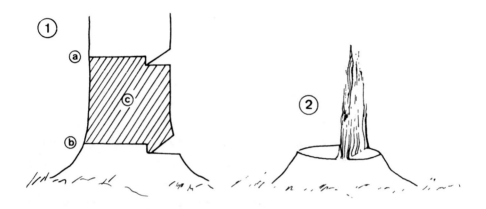

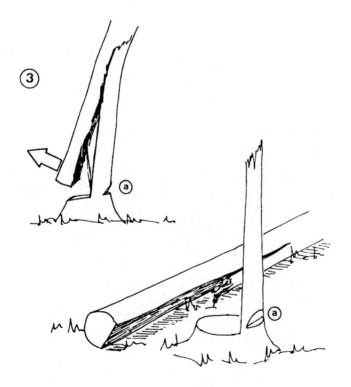

WOOD WASTAGE DUE TO POOR WORKING TECHNIQUES IN FELLING (continued)

A considerable amount of valuable wood is lost when large trees
are felled across obstacles on the ground such as hollows **(1)**,
ridges **(2)**, logs or rocks **(3)**. Most species break if they hit
such obstacles. Although the broken part may be small, the loss
caused by cutting out the break can be considerable.

The experienced worker will look carefully for obstacles and,
when determining the felling direction, he will try to avoid them.
This will be possible in many cases. Remember that even heavily
leaning trees can be felled to a point about 30° on either side
of the lean.

Efforts to avoid obstructions not only reduce waste but also
facilitate work because unnecessary cross-cutting is avoided.

The breaking of a tree can cause serious losses, especially for
valuable hardwood species.

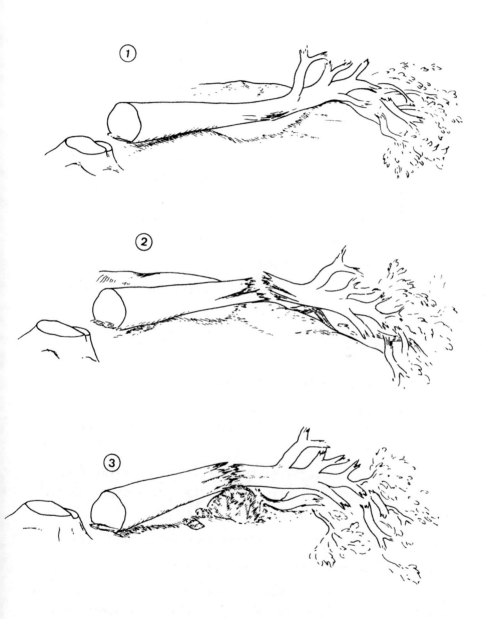

RELEASING LODGED TREES WITH SIMPLE TOOLS

When thinning man-made forests, falling trees are frequently
stopped by other trees. The tree is then said to be lodged and
this is called a hang-up.

Skilled operators will try to avoid this by felling the tree into
open spaces. A proper undercut, an adequate hinge and wedging
will help to reduce lodging, but this cannot always be avoided.

BEWARE - dislodging hung-up trees is very dangerous. Think first
before deciding how to take the tree down.

Do not walk or work below a hang-up.

Do not try to fell the tree which is holding the lodged tree.

Do not fell another tree on to the hang-up.

Do not climb the lodged tree to loosen its crown.

Recommended techniques for small trees

- Place suitable material (e.g. poles, split wood) on the
  ground on to which the tree might slide backwards **(1a)**,
  (2a), **(3a)**.

- Cut the remaining wood which may still connect the tree with
  the stump, preferably with an axe **(1)**. If a saw is used, it
  might easily get pinched.

- Use the turning hook to roll the tree to one side **(2)**.

- Use a pole to push the butt end backwards **(3)**.

- Use a manual winch to pull the tree backwards **(4)**. A pulley
  may help to increase the pull or to place the winch in a
  safe position, if necessary.

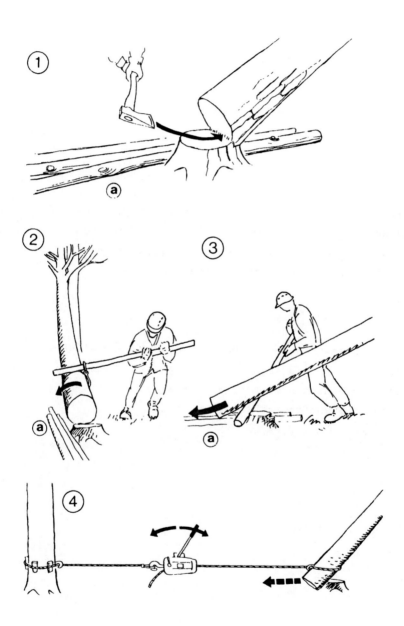

RELEASING LODGED TREES WITH SPECIAL EQUIPMENT AND MACHINES

If lodging occurs frequently, a sulky may be a convenient aid for
lifting the tree up from the stump and to pull it down (1). The
sulky may also be used to skid it to the skidding line. Sulkies
are an excellent means of facilitating this heavy and dangerous
job. Their use is restricted to trees up to a volume of about
0.5 cubic metres. Sulkies can be made in local workshops.

BEWARE - if the terrain slopes, the tree may push the sulky
suddenly forward when it is lifted from the stump. In such cases,
it is advisable to move the butt end to the ground before attach-
ing the sulky. For braking, the handle of the sulky is lifted up.

Heavy trees which cannot be dislodged by manual work should be
pulled down with draught animals or a skidding tractor (2). The
tractor or animals must be placed at a safe distance from the
lodged tree and the cable winch used.

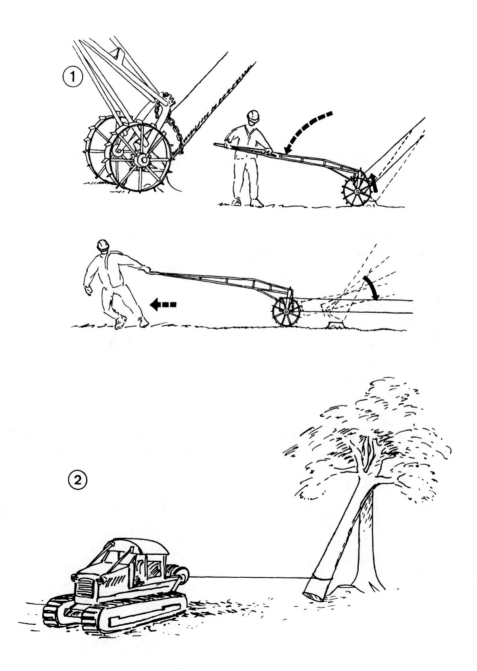

DEBRANCHING

Debranching may be a rather time-consuming job, especially in coniferous trees. It is done with an axe. For small poles with thin branches, a matchet can also be used.

Debranching is a dangerous job and easily causes accidents which may be quite severe, especially if a powerful stroke misses the branch and hits the leg. This may happen especially to young, inexperienced workers.

It is therefore essential never to cut towards the legs, to stand as far as possible on the side of the tree opposite the branch that is cut (1) and always to direct the stroke away from the body.

Debranching usually proceeds towards the top of the tree. If branches are thick and under tension, it may be preferable first to cut them off some distance from their base and subsequently cut the remaining part flush with the stem.

If trees are heavily branched, care must be taken to remove cut branches from the tree and to keep the working space clear.

After debranching the upper side, a turning hook (2) is needed to turn trees or logs (2a).

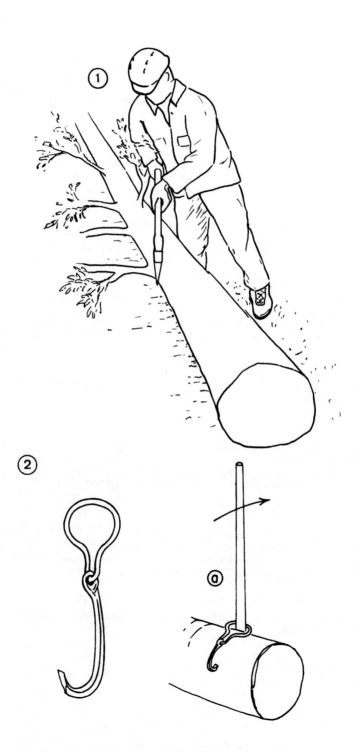

DEBARKING

Debarking of wood may be required for a variety of reasons such
as control of insects, acceleration of wood seasoning, reduction
of weight in transport or simply the demand for wood without bark,
for instance pulp wood, or the demand for the bark itself if it
is used for tanning.

Large industries requiring debarked wood are usually equipped
with debarking machines installed in the plant.

If manual debarking is required, a variety of different tools can
be used. As debarking demands much time and effort, the tools
should be suitable for the job and be handled efficiently.

Debarking of small- to medium-sized logs is usually done with debarking spades, of which different models exist. A short-handled
debarking spade is used for harder bark **(1a)**, a long-handled one
for softer bark, to permit working in longer strokes **(1b)**.

Axes may be used to debark trees or their butt ends if the bark is
too thick and tough for the debarking spade.

It may be necessary to debark large logs of broad-leaved tropical
trees which have very thick and strong bark. In such cases, an
iron spoon should be used which permits, if necessary, beating the
bark loose and peeling it off with the spoon **(2)**.

Machetes are sometimes used for peeling off the thin bark of
smaller trees, such as eucalyptus. They are less efficient and
less convenient than debarking spades and should therefore be
restricted to occasional work on a small scale.

As in debranching, a turning hook may be needed to turn logs
during debarking.

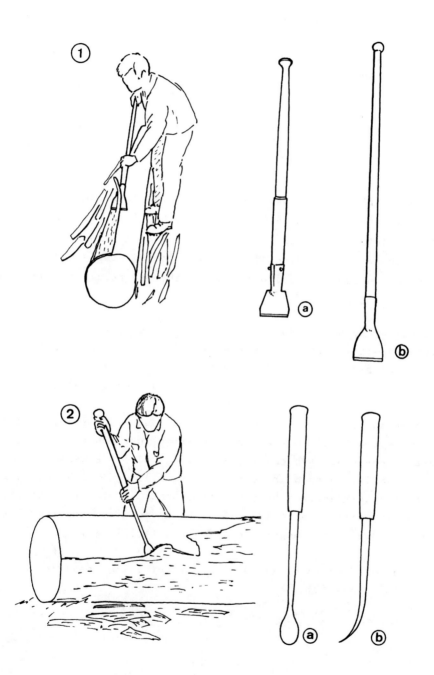

GENERAL RULES FOR CROSS-CUTTING

If the tree is not skidded to a landing for cross-cutting, this
operation should be done in the forest by the same team which
does the felling and debranching to avoid delays and additional
time spent on getting to the tree. However, this process requires
the presence of qualified supervisors or availability of workers
having basic knowledge in timber grading unless only fuelwood is
to be produced.

The greatest care is required to avoid losses in cross-cutting
valuable trees. They should be thoroughly inspected for proper
grading before cross-cutting begins. Clear instructions should
be given for the grading of different logs. Simply cutting trees
from the bottom into uniform log lengths may result in much wastage
during utilisation.

A single tree may be cut into different assortments: for instance,
higher-quality logs for the sawmill (1a), lower-quality logs for a
chipboard plant (1b), and fuelwood (1c). Skilled grading can considerably increase the economic returns of the operation.

In many sawmills, it is common for saw logs to go straight from
the forest without further cross-cutting into conversion. In such
cases, tree shape and quality must be carefully assessed to allow
a reasonable degree of recovery in the mill. Heavily tapering
trees should therefore be cut into shorter lengths than straight
trees with little taper (2). Minimum and maximum log length and
size, however, will depend on transport facilities.

Crooked logs should normally be cross-cut in the bend and not between the bends (3).

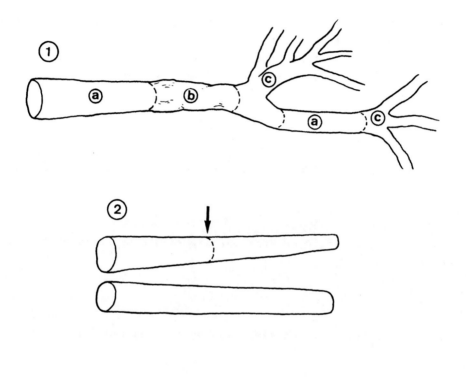

TOOLS FOR CROSS-CUTTING

For cross-cutting small-sized trees, e.g. for fuelwood, a portable support should be used **(1)**. This facilitates the job and avoids contact of the sharp cutting tool with the ground. This type of support can easily be made on the spot and transported within the forest (see page 92).

Bow saws are handy for cross-cutting up to a diameter of 20 cm **(2)**.

Above diameters of 20 cm, the bow saw should be replaced by the cross-cut saw **(3)**.

To avoid pinching of the saw, wedging is required **(4)**.

Furthermore, tools for correct measuring are needed, such as measuring sticks, tapes or calipers.

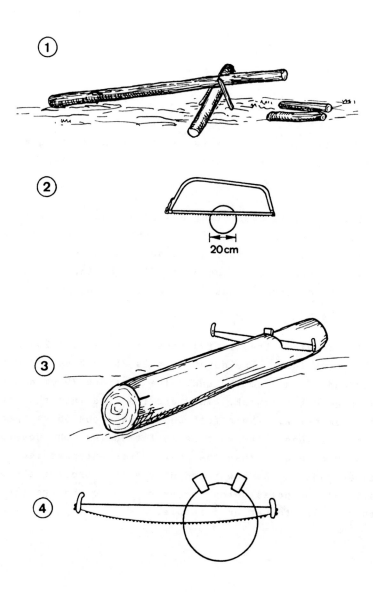

20 cm

SUPPORTS AND TRESTLES

These are made locally and used as an aid for work such as debarking and cross-cutting in the stand, at the roadside, landing
or timber yard. In many cases, work is done more easily and
quickly when using supports and trestles. Moreover, tool edges
remain sharp for a longer time if work is not done close to the
ground.

A forked branch is the easiest means of supporting a pole if
rested against a standing tree in the forest (1).

Dovetail trestles consist of a wooden post and two legs. They
can easily be made in the forest with no other tools than an axe
and a bow saw. Dry and light wood is used. Two dovetail cuts
are made on one end of the post (2). The top ends of the legs
are square on three sides (3) and fitted into the dovetail cuts.

The low dovetail trestle (4) consists of a post 200 cm long and
12 cm thick (4a). The dovetail cuts 25 mm deep are made about
20 cm and 40 cm from the end. The legs are 70 cm and 80 cm long
and about 7.5 cm thick. They are inserted into the dovetail
cuts from below. Their feet should be about 65 cm apart. The
top of the longer leg must be so fitted into the dovetail that
it is 10 cm higher than the post. This extended leg and two
notches made in the lower end of the post provide three resting
positions for poles which can be put on to the trestle by tools
such as a log turner or a sappie.

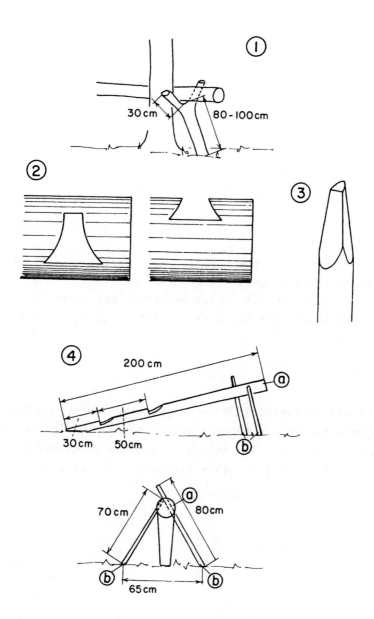

CROSS-CUTTING OF TREES UNDER TENSION

Cross-cutting of trees under tension may cause loss of wood and may also pinch the saw. This should be avoided as much as possible through special techniques.

Tension can often be reduced by putting supports under the tree **(1a)**. If this is not possible, e.g. in a tree where the upper side is under tension and the lower side is accessible, then cross-cutting should be done from below **(1b)** until the saw starts jamming and then continued from above **(1c)**.

If the lower side of the tree is under tension, an effort should be made to place a support under the tree **(2a)**. In this case, sawing should start from above until the saw starts jamming **(2b)** and be continued from below **(2c)** unless wedging is feasible and sufficient.

In windfalls, cross-cutting under tension is very common. As shown on pages 98 and 99, a pressure rope or cable can be used in such cases to avoid cracking. Such equipment may in special cases also be useful in other harvesting operations.

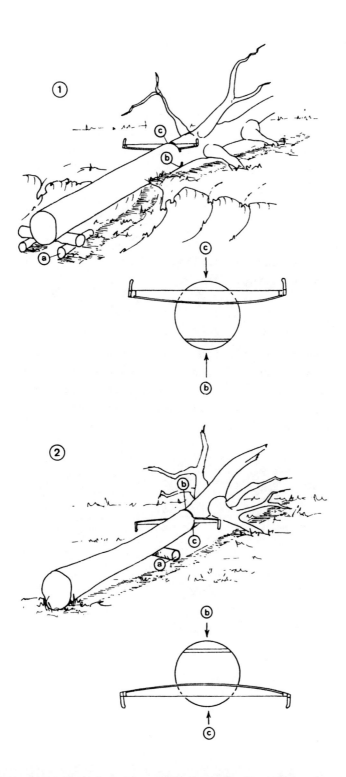

WOOD WASTAGE IN CROSS-CUTTING

Cross-cutting with axes should be avoided **(1a)**. In large-sized
wood, losses of 30 per cent of the total volume may occur if wood
is cut into lengths of 1 m or less. The saw cut wastes only a
minimal amount of wood and requires less effort than axe work
(1b). Furthermore, a clean saw cut allows more precise measure-
ment and stacking as well as denser loading in transport.

If cross-cuts on logs are not made at an angle of 90° **(2a)**, wood
is usually lost during utilisation since logs may require cor-
rective cross-cutting.

Cutting from the side which is under tension causes the log to
crack. This may be an advantage in special circumstances when
the log would have to be split anyway into fuelwood or pulpwood.
However, valuable logs should never be reduced by careless cutting
to fuelwood quality **(3a, 3b)**.

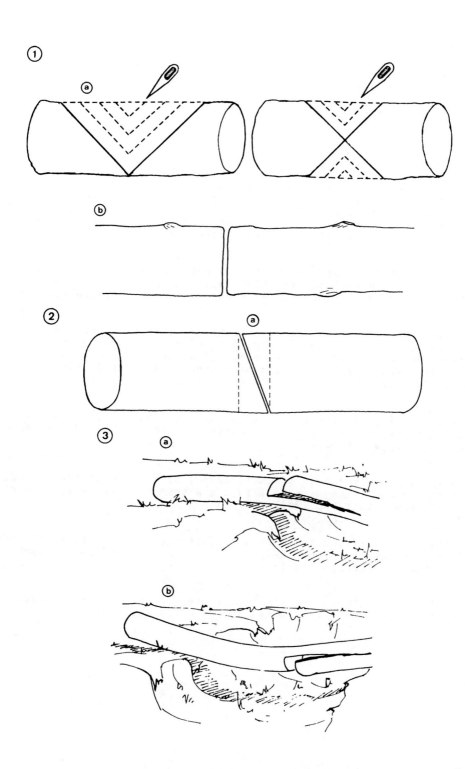

Windfalls are dangerous to cut: the wood is often under high
tension; the working place is sometimes restricted and the tree
difficult to get at. Stumps may tip forward or backward when cut
loose from the trunk. Therefore, the worker must be well trained
and experienced in order to avoid accidents and to reduce the loss
of wood.

Chain saws have a definite advantage over hand saws in clearing
windfalls as they can be more easily handled in restricted space
and, compared to a cross-cut saw, only one man is exposed to
danger. They permit special techniques for cutting wood under
tension without cracking. Furthermore, in extensive windfalls
where there is a danger of wood deterioration through insects and
fungi, chain saws help to speed up the operation.

Wind-fallen areas are attacked from the side where the wind has
entered. When working with hand tools, trees are worked up from
the top end by debranching and cross-cutting to release tension.

When cutting the tree from the stump, special care must be taken
if there is a danger of the stump turning over. To avoid the
stump moving towards the sawyers, different means of support can
be used, e.g. a piece of wood or a stone (1a), a pole (1b), or
a cable (1c).

After cutting off the tree, stumps may fall back. The sawyers
must therefore make sure that nobody is standing behind the stump
whilst they are sawing.

In loose soil, the base of the tree may be pressed on the ground.
In this case, it is necessary to dig a trench to allow salvage of
the valuable butt end (2a).

Cutting of tensioned trees in windfalls may easily result in wood
losses through cracking (2b). This risk can be reduced through
pressure ropes or chains (3).

Work in windfalls is greatly facilitated if the wood is skidded
after cross-cutting to storage places which are easy of access.

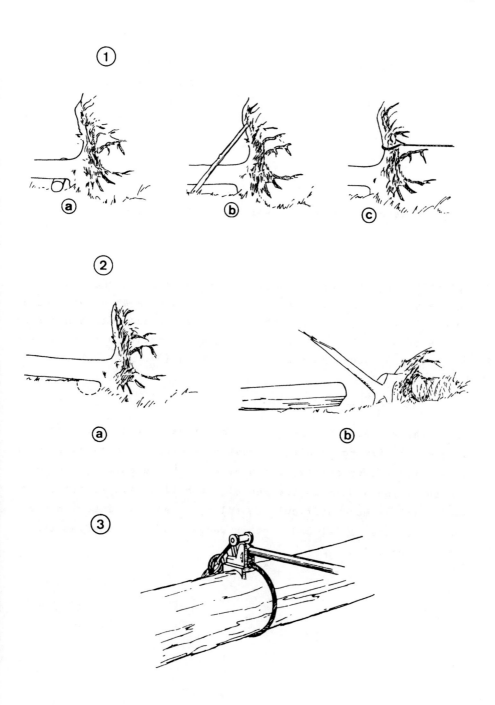

To make handling and transport of short pieces of wood easier and
to reduce the time required for seasoning, wood of a diameter ex-
ceeding 20 cm is often split after cross-cutting. In the absence
of splitting tools, bigger wood pieces of fuelwood quality often
remain unutilised.

It may also be necessary to split wood to be used as fence posts.

Splitting requires good quality splitting hammers and wedges.
The hammer should weigh about 2.5 kg and have a straight handle,
about 90 cm long, with a knob (1). Steel wedges with a mushroom
head should not be used (2). The safest wedge is a steel socket
wedge with a wooden head and a steel ring (3).

Since the way wood splits differs a lot depending on the tree
species, splitting techniques must be modified accordingly. For
wood which splits easily, a few blows with the cutting side of
the splitting hammer on the end of the billet will suffice. For
wood which is more difficult to split, a wedge is inserted near
the end of the billet and further wedges may be needed as the
crack opens (3).

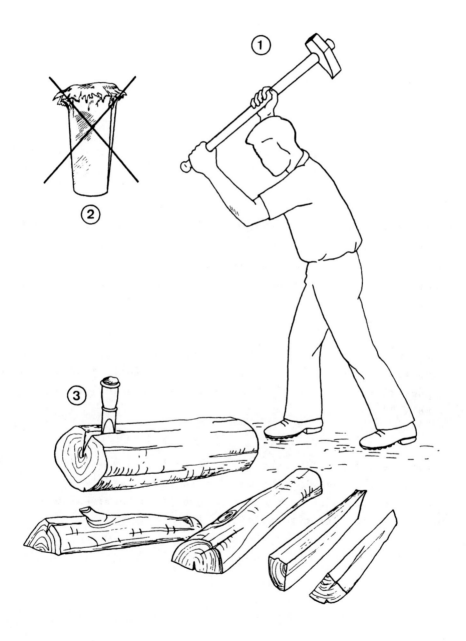

HANDLING BILLETS AND LOGS

Loading and stacking of billets and moving of logs is easier if
simple helping tools are used.

In the absence of such helping tools, the worker has to bend down
and pick up the wood from the ground, which may be muddy **(1a)**.

A timber pick makes it much easier to pick up and handle small
pieces of wood **(1b)**.

Different types of handling tools are available, such as metal
hooks **(2)**, timber picks with a short wooden handle, fitting the
hand of the worker **(3)** and small timber tongs **(4)**. The latter
tool is particularly handy but the former ones can be locally
made more easily.

The sappie is used for lifting or for short-distance skidding of
logs **(5)**. A model for heavier logs has a handle 190 cm long and
a hook 42 cm long. A lighter model has a handle 110 cm long and
a hook 28 cm long.

Sappies are typically used for pulling logs **(6)** and for turning
them **(7)**. In the Alpine countries they were widely used for
gravity skidding of logs and continue to be indispensable in
handling logs during tree felling and transport.

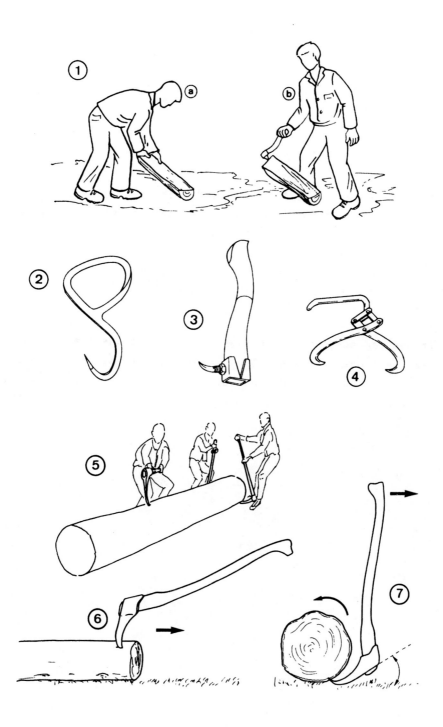

MANUAL TRANSPORT OF SMALLER-SIZED WOOD

Carrying wood manually should be avoided as much as possible. It
is a heavy and inefficient job which is only permissible over
short distances of just a few metres **(1)**.

Small logs can be pulled more easily to the stacking or loading
place using skidding tongs **(2)**. The tong should be attached
close to the end of the log to achieve a lifting effect and thus
facilitate pulling.

If the terrain and ground cover permit, the wheelbarrow is an
excellent means of assembling loads of short pieces of wood for
transport over short distances, e.g. for taking wood to a site
for a charcoal kiln **(3)**.

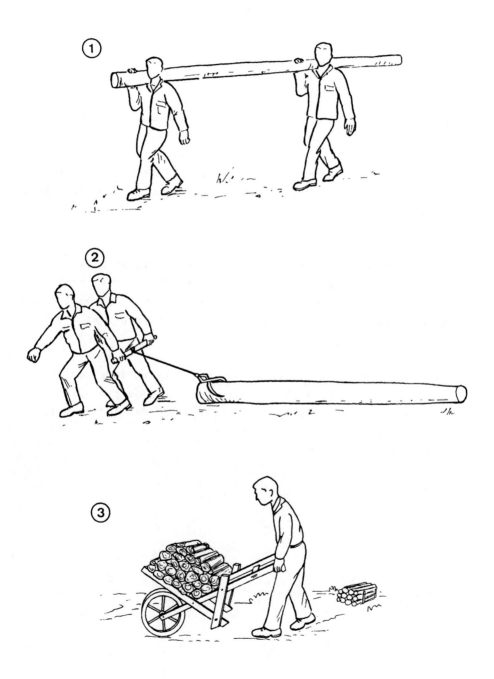

USE OF SKIDDING SULKIES

The skidding sulky **(1)** is used for short-distance transport of
small-sized logs, especially downhill on moderate slopes. Loads
can consist of single logs or bundles and may have a weight of
up to 200 kg. On flat terrain, loads are attached at the centre
of gravity. On increasing slopes, the load is shifted more towards the back to serve as a brake. Skidding sulkies can be
built with 2 wheels **(1a)** or with 4 wheels fixed to bogie axles
(1b). The latter type is more sophisticated but permits the
handling of larger loads and negotiating rougher surface conditions.

Two sulkies can also be connected to skid bigger logs **(2).** In
this case, the load is guided by one handle in the front and one
in the rear. On slopes, the rear part of the log should hang
close to the ground to facilitate rapid braking when required.

On steep terrain, two sulkies may be operated together **(3).** They
can be connected by a cable which is guided by two pulleys attached to trees **(3a).** The loaded sulky **(3b)** can thus be used to
pull up the empty one **(3c),** together with the worker, who guides
it by the handle.

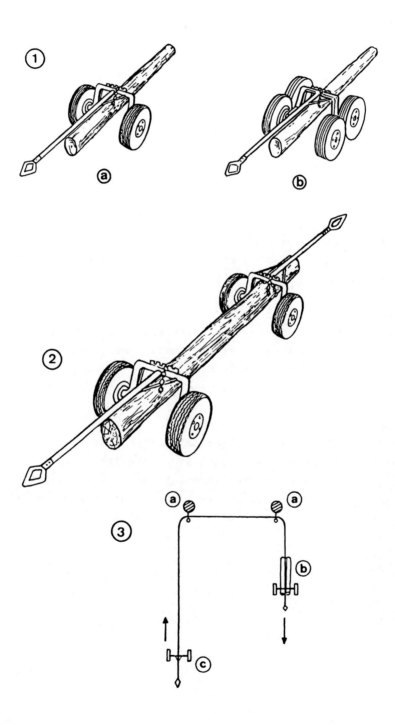

SLIDING WOOD DOWNHILL

Timber chutes are used for sliding small logs or short pieces of
wood downhill on slopes with a gradient of 25% or more **(1)**.

Plastic chutes are commercially available in sections of 5 m and
with a diameter of 35-50 cm. At a diameter of 40 cm, the chutes
can take logs up to a length of 5 m and short pieces to a diameter
of 30 cm.

Chutes may be used over distances of up to 150 m. Under favour-
able conditions, 2 m^3 stacked may be transported per hour over
that distance.

Commercially-available chutes are easily assembled thanks to
different connecting systems. Chutes may be made locally from
plastic tubes cut lengthwise or from other materials, e.g. wooden
boards, although these are heavier and more difficult to handle.

In clearfelling areas on moderate slopes, logs may be rolled down
to the roadside across trees which have been felled up the slope
(2). They can subsequently be cut into shorter assortments, if
necessary, at the foot of the slope. This technique, if applied
properly, can save considerable expense in skidding.

Proper stacking of wood at the roadside prior to transport aids
seasoning, reduces weight and provides protection against deterioration. Stacking should if possible be done on the higher side of
the road embankment if this facilitates loading **(1)**.

Logs and poles should be placed on supports **(1a)** and be easily
accessible for loading.

Short wood is usually piled in stacks which also require supports
(2a). The stacks should be firmly secured by one or more stakes
(2b).

Small-sized material used for fuel can be bundled prior to stacking
and is thus more easily handled and marketed **(3)**.

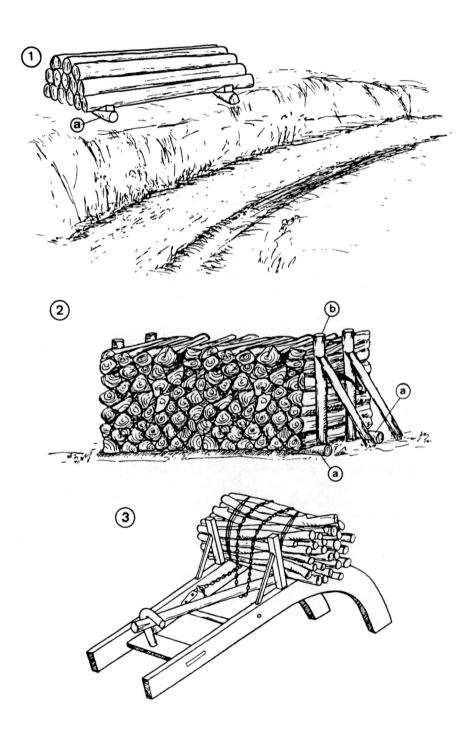

Pit-sawing continues to be widespread in rural areas of developing
countries. It is used for cutting boards and planks at the felling
site without transporting the logs. The sawnwood is mainly used
locally as building material but sometimes it reaches distant mar-
kets. Pit-sawing provides jobs for many thousands of workers.

Pits are dug and large logs are easily rolled across for sawing.
However, it is more convenient to set up a stand on which the log
is placed (1). The saw cut is marked with a string soaked in moist
charcoal dust (fines). A plumb line is fixed to the end of the cut
to guide the worker standing on the ground. This worker should
wear a wide-brimmed hat as a protection against sawdust. The saw
cuts only on the way down but the worker standing on the log has
the heavier job because he has to lift the saw up to shoulder
height. Therefore, both workers should change places regularly.

The pit saw is tapering in shape (2). Depending on log size, pit
saws may vary in length from 150 to 300 cm. Different types of
handles are used. An example is given of a lower handle (3a) and
an upper handle (3b), both of which must be easily removable.

The shape and size of the teeth is indicated in illustration 4.
The height of teeth is from 15 to 20 mm, the distance from tooth
to tooth from 20 to 25 mm, the front edge angle varies from
100 to 105° and the near edge angle from 20 to 25 mm.

Maintenance includes the following operations:

-   jointing (as for cross-cut saws);

-   gulleting (with round-edge millsaw file);

-   sharpening of teeth (with millsaw at an angle of 90° with
    the saw);

-   setting of saw (as for triangular cross-cut saws, saw set
    0.8 mm);

-   bevelling (teeth pointing away are given a slight bevel of
    about 5°).

The measures given must be adapted to size of log and hardness of
wood.

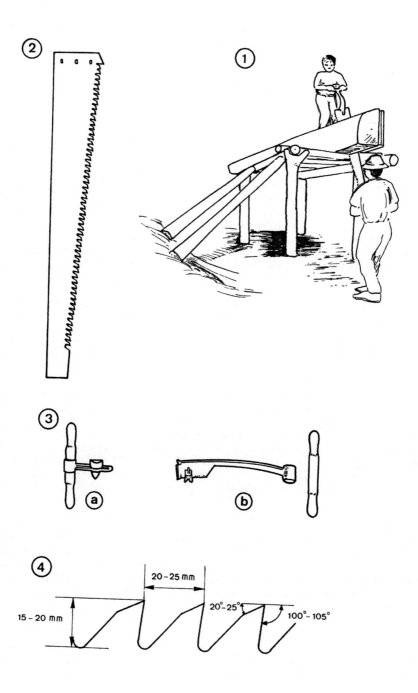

Wood harvesting, whether done with hand tools or with machines,
can be a heavy and dangerous job. If it is done by unskilled persons with poor tools and inadequate working techniques, it generally
results in excessive effort, numerous accidents, low productivity
and also in wood waste. For this reason, training is indispensable
not only for professional forest workers but also for occasional
wood cutters such as rural people harvesting fuelwood or constructio
poles.

Obviously, such training must be adapted to the special conditions
of wood harvesting. It must be done on the job, as much as possible
in a practical way and on a short-term basis with follow-up visits.
It should always be based on locally-available tools and equipment.
The benefits of training may be lost if tools are brought just for
the sake of training which cannot be bought locally or which are
too expensive for village people. Under such conditions, it is
important for the trainer to ensure that tools and tool handles
made by rural artisans or sold by local hardware shops meet the
requirements as much as possible.

Traditionally, skills are passed on from one generation to the next.
Where the axe is the only wood harvesting tool, this transfer of
skills normally produces quite experienced axe workers. However,
the use of saws, saw maintenance tools and helping tools requires
additional knowledge and skill for which training is needed.

Training of professional forest workers may last several weeks in
order to reach acceptable levels of productivity with new tools
and working methods. For the occasional wood cutter, the minimum
would be a one-to-two day demonstration, but a one-week period
including demonstrations and on-the-job practice would be preferable. This type of training should concentrate on safe working
habits, reduction of physical effort and optimal wood utilisation
more than on high productivity.

The trainee is provided with information, demonstrations and practice regarding tools and tool maintenance, safety rules, directiona
tree felling, debranching, cross-cutting, splitting, stacking and
transport as required for his job. For the maintenance of tools,
especially saws and wooden handles, it may be necessary to train
specially selected persons who take care of this aspect for a group
of workers.

Training will be readily accepted if it brings obvious benefits to
the trainee. Follow-up visits are needed to further improve and
correct the work.

The instructor plays a crucial role in training. He will only be accepted if he is perfectly skilled himself and if he is able to communicate in the language spoken locally. Ideally, instructors should themselves have extensive experience in wood harvesting and should undergo special training as instructors for several months.

Training of instructors for wood harvesting is included in ILO technical co-operation activities. Further information on this subject may be requested from:

>   Forestry and Wood Industries Specialist,
>   International Labour Office,
>   CH-1211 GENEVA 22,
>   Switzerland.

Please send any comments which you might wish to make on the contents of this training manual and suggestions for its improvement to the same address.

CPSIA information can be obtained at www.ICGtesting.com
Printed in the USA
LVOW10s1235251013

358586LV00003B/98/A